lock, stock
& two smoking barrels

This publication is not authorised for sale in
the United States of America and/or Canada

WISE PUBLICATIONS
London / New York / Sydney / Paris / Copenhagen / Madrid

Exclusive Distributors:
Music Sales Limited
8/9 Frith Street, London W1V 5TZ,
England.
Music Sales Pty Limited
120 Rothschild Avenue, Rosebery, NSW 2018,
Australia.

Order No.AM954591
ISBN 0-7119-7283-4
This book © Copyright 1998
by Wise Publications.
Visit the Internet Music Shop at
http://www.musicsales.co.uk

Unauthorised reproduction of any
part of this publication by any means
including photocopying is an infringement
of copyright.

Music arranged by Derek Jones.
Music processed by Paul Ewers Music Design.
Photographs courtesy of Sebastian Pearson /
PolyGram Filmed Entertainment.

Printed in the United Kingdom by
Printwise (Haverhill) Limited, Suffolk.

Your Guarantee of Quality:
As publishers, we strive to produce every
book to the highest commercial standards.
The music has been freshly engraved
and the book has been carefully
designed to minimise awkward page
turns and to make playing from it a real
pleasure. Particular care has been given
to specifying acid-free, neutral-sized
paper made from pulps which have not
been elemental chlorine bleached.
This pulp is from farmed sustainable
forests and was produced with special
regard for the environment.
Throughout, the printing and binding
have been planned to ensure a sturdy,
attractive publication which should give
years of enjoyment.
If your copy fails to meet our high
standards, please inform us and we will
gladly replace it.

Music Sales' complete catalogue
describes thousands of titles and is
available in full colour sections by subject,
direct from Music Sales Limited.
Please state your areas of interest and
send a cheque/postal order for £1.50
for postage to: Music Sales Limited,
Newmarket Road, Bury St. Edmunds,
Suffolk IP33 3YB.

HUNDRED MILE HIGH CITY

WORDS & MUSIC BY SIMON FOWLER, STEVE CRADOCK, DAMON MINCHELLA & OSCAR HARRISON

1. So I said— I'm on the road— so I need— a car, and I know—
(Verses 2 & 3 see block lyric)

© Copyright 1997 Island Music Limited, 47 British Grove, London W4.
All Rights Reserved. International Copyright Secured.

I be - lieve it.

Verse 2:
Well I want a good love on my side
Keep on getting out love on my pride
But I know I keep hurting my love yeah,
But I know it ain't killing.

Verse 3:
So I said I'm on the road so I need a car,
And I know that I'm staying alive.
But I know that my faith is in season
But I say that it's living.

THE BOSS

WORDS & MUSIC BY JAMES BROWN, CHARLES BOBBITT & FRED WESLEY

Paid the cost to be the boss.

Paid the cost to be the boss. I've

paid the cost to be the boss. Look at me. You know what to

© Copyright 1973 Dijon Music Publications/Dyatone Publishing Company, USA.
PolyGram Music Publishing Limited, 47 British Grove, London W4 (75%)/Copyright Control (25%).
All Rights Reserved. International Copyright Secured.

see. See a bad moth-er.

Huh!

Huh! Told you so.

Told you so. Hav-in' fun,— I got might-y fine.___

16

Hav-in' fun,_____ I got might-y fine.   Hav-in' fun,_____ I got might-y fine.

_____   Hav-in' fun,—   I got might-y fine.   Got- ta

pay the cost—   to be the boss.   Paid the cost_____   to be the

boss.—   Paid the cost_____   to be the   boss.

Con - tract— sir.　　　Turn my back— sir.　　　Con - tract— sir.

Turn my back— sir.　　　Paid the cost—　　　to be the

boss.　　　I'm a bad mo- ther.　　　Huh!

I'm a bad mo- ther.

Headin' for the turnaround.

I'm headin' for the turnaround.

Told— you so.

Repeat ad lib. to fade

TRULY, MADLY, DEEPLY

WORDS & MUSIC BY CRAIG STEVENS, SEAN FLOWERDEW & GRAEME FLOWERDEW

Red light shin - ing bright - ly, must be a warn - ing.

Dan - ger can be -

© Copyright 1997 Sony/ATV Music Publishing. 10 Great Marlborough Street. London W1.
All Rights Reserved. International Copyright Secured.

so ad-dic-ted to me. Sound is

down but si-lence is not a-round me.

(2° see block lyric)

Your sweet voice a-lone drifts through my

mind.

I feel no pain, the pain has gone now.

The pain has gone now, now. What I feel won't change,

always remains the same. Tru-

-ly hooked on you. Mad-ly stuck on you. Deep-ly, I feel no

pain.— Tru - ly hooked—on you. Mad - ly stuck—on you. Deep

1.

- ly—— re - mains the— same.—

My vi -

2.(%)

same.— Tru - ly hooked—on you. Mad - ly stuck—on you. Deep

-ly,___ I feel no___ pain.___ Tru - ly hooked___ on you. Mad-

-ly stuck___ on you. Deep - ly___ re - mains the___ same.___

D.𝄋. *Repeat chorus to fade*

2°:
My vision is so blurred
Only you I see clearly now
And it leaves an everlasting
Impression on my mind
I feel no pain
The pain has gone now
What I feel won't change
Always remains the same.

Truly, *etc*.

POLICE AND THIEVES

MUSIC BY LEE PERRY. WORDS BY JUNIOR MURVIN

© Copyright 1976 Songs Of PolyGram International. Island Music Limited, 47 British Grove, London W4.
All Rights Reserved. International Copyright Secured.

18 WITH A BULLET

WORDS & MUSIC BY PETE WINGFIELD

♩. = 75

Ow! Well____ darl - ing,____ well, well, well,__ well,

well, well,__ well.__ Oh____ yeah____ oh,__ oh.__

1. I'm eigh - teen__ with a bul - let,
(Verses 2 & 3 see block lyrics)

© Copyright 1974 Island Music Limited/Uncle Doris Limited. 47 British Grove. London W4.
All Rights Reserved. International Copyright Secured.

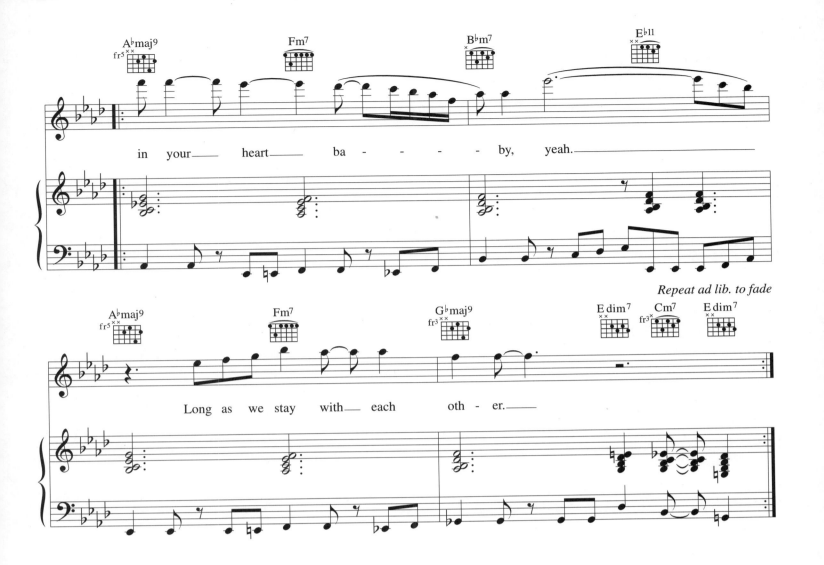

Repeat ad lib. to fade

Verse 2:
I'm eighteen with a bullet
Got my finger on the trigger
I'm gonna pull it.
I'm a super soul sureshot, papa
I'm a national breakout
So let me check your playlist, baby
Come on, and let's make out.

I'm high on the chart
I'm tipped for the top
Until I'm in your heart
I ain't never gonna stop
Never, baby.

Verse 3:
I'm eighteen with a bullet
Got my finger on the trigger
I wanna pull it, huh
Be my 'A' side, baby
'B' side me
Right now I'm a single
But pretty soon you'll see.

SPOOKY

WORDS & MUSIC BY HARRY MIDDLEBROOKS & MIKE SHAPIRO

1. In the cool of the eve-nin' when ev-'ry-thing is get-tin' kind of
(Verses 2 & 3 see block lyrics)

groo - vy,___ you call me up and ask me would I

© Copyright 1970 Lowery Music Company Incorporated, USA.
BMG Music Publishing Limited, Bedford House, 69-79 Fulham High Street, London SW6.
This arrangement © Copyright 1998 BMG Music Publishing Limited.
All Rights Reserved. International Copyright Secured.

⊕ *Coda*

spoo - ky. Ba—
ba— ba— spoo - ky. Mm— mm.

Repeat ad lib. to fade

Verse 2:
You always keep me guessing
I never seem to know what you are thinking
And if a girl looks at you
It's for sure your little eye will be a-winking
I get confused, I never know where I stand
And then you smile and hold my hand
Love is kinda crazy with a spooky little boy like you.

Verse 3:
If you decide someday
To stop this little game that you are playing
I'm gonna tell you all the things
My heart's been a-dying to be saying
Just like a ghost
You've been a-hauntin' my dreams
But now I know you're not what you seem
Love is kinda crazy with a spooky little boy like you.

MAN MACHINE

WORDS & MUSIC BY GUY CHAMBERS & ROBBIE WILLIAMS

1. Sit - ting in the cheap seats un - der - neath the stars. ___
(Verse 2 see block lyric)

I'm head - ing back to base, I'll drop you off at my ___

© Copyright 1998 EMI Virgin Music Limited, 127 Charing Cross Road. London WC2 (50%) &
BMG Music Publishing Limited, 69-79 Fulham High Street. London SW6 (50%).
This arrangement © 1998 BMG Music Publishing Limited for their share of interest.
All Rights Reserved. International Copyright Secured.

Verse 2:
How you gonna leave when your bags ain't packed?
And how you gonna shoot when we're back to back?
How do you tell a joke when you can't laugh?
You know the other punchline, better take a bath.

I'm a man machine *etc.*

WHY DID YOU DO IT

WORDS & MUSIC BY GRAHAM KIRBY

1, 3. I've been think-ing 'bout— what you have done to me,— the
(Verse 2 see block lyric)

(Vocals 8ve on D.%.)

© Copyright 1975 Palan Music Publishing Limited. Greenland Place. 115-123 Bayham Street. London NW1.
All Rights Reserved. International Copyright Secured.

damage is____ much deep - er than____ you'll ev - er see.____

Hit me like a ham-mer to____ my head,____

I

won - der were____ you____ pushed or were you led?____

Why did you do____ it? Why did you do____ that thing____ to me?____

Why did you do— it?

Why did you do— that thing— to me?—

The on-ly one who knows— the truth,—

man— that's him,— me and you.—

Verse 2:
My friends, they listen to the things I say
They listen and they hear more every day
But I know they never understand it
Because it was no accident - you planned it.

Why did you do it *etc.*

OH GIRL

WORDS & MUSIC BY MAURO PAWLOWSKI

© Copyright 1998 Copyright Control.
All Rights Reserved. International Copyright Secured.

Hot fun in the hot sun

with a friend - ly wel - come.

FOOLS GOLD

WORDS & MUSIC BY IAN BROWN & JOHN SQUIRE

Gold road's sure a long____ road,_____
(% see block lyric)

1. 2. The

© Copyright 1989 Zomba Music Publishers Limited, 165-167 High Road, London NW10.
All Rights Reserved. International Copyright Secured.

winds on through the hills___ for fif - teen days.

The pack on my back is ach - ing, the

To Coda ⊕

straps seem to cut me like a knife.___

I'm no clown I won't back down, I don't need you to tell___ me what's go-ing

down.

Down   down___   down___

down, da down, down, down.

Down, down,— down,— down, da down, down, down.

Am   C

G   Am

I'm stand-ing a-lone,

you're weigh-ing your gold,____ I'm watch-ing you sink - ing.____

Fool's_____ gold.

Repeat to fade

Verse 3:
These boots were made for walking
The Marquis de Sade never made no boots like these
Gold's just around the corner
Breakdown's coming up 'round the bend.

18 WITH A BULLET

WORDS & MUSIC BY PETE WINGFIELD

© Copyright 1974 Island Music Limited/Uncle Doris Limited, 47 British Grove, London W4.
All Rights Reserved. International Copyright Secured.

Verse 2:

I'm eighteen with a bullet
Got my finger on the trigger
I'm gonna pull it.
I'm a super soul sureshot, yeah
I'm a national breakout
So let me check your playlist, mama
Come on, let's make out.

I'm high on the chart
I'm tipped for the top
Until I'm in your heart
I ain't never gonna stop
Never, never baby.

Verse 3:

I'm eighteen with a bullet
Got my finger on the trigger
I'm gonna pull it, yes I am
Be my 'A' side, baby
Be 'B' side me
Right now, right now I'm a single
But pretty soon you'll see.